Adapted by Tatty Hennessy

ISBN 978-0-573-13372-5

concordtheatricals.co.uk
concordtheatricals.com

FOR AMATEUR PRODUCTION ENQUIRIES

UNITED KINGDOM AND WORLD
EXCLUDING NORTH AMERICA
licensing@concordtheatricals.co.uk
020-7054-7298

Each title is subject to availability from Concord Theatricals, depending upon country of performance.

This work is published by Samuel French, an imprint of Concord Theatricals Ltd.

CAST

KIRSTY FERRIGGI | VIV

Kirsty is a visually impaired actress and recent graduate of Drama Studio London. *The Sleeping Sword* marks Kirsty's professional debut. Theatre credits while training include: *The Illusion of Time, Hamlet, A Midsummer Night's Dream, Tartuffe, Enemy of the People, The One* and *The Last Days of Judas Iscariot.*

AARIAN MEHRABANI | BUN

Aarian graduated from the Royal Central School of Speech and Drama in 2020.

Theatre credits include: *Guy: A New Musical* (UK Tour); *BRINK* and *Nothing* (Royal Exchange Theatre).

Aarian also works as a deviser and facilitator, as well as writing and performing his own music under the name 'Aarian'. His debut single *Five Yard Line* was released on all streaming services in May 2022. In 2021 he co-founded the award-winning theatre company FlawBored who are currently developing their debut show.

TIKA MU'TAMIR | ANNA

Tika is a graduate from East 15 Acting School and Middlesex University and performs between the UK and Malaysia.

Theatre credits include: *The Tempest* (The Handlebards UK Tour); *Me & My Bee* (National Theatre: River Stage) and a range of Shakespeare plays travelling to theatres and schools across South East Asia.

Tika predominantly and passionately involves herself in educational and community theatre – her skills and true joy lie in movement, devising and heart-led projects.

DANIEL RYAN | AUDIOBOOK NARRATOR

Daniel is a stage and screen actor, recognisable from his roles on some of the nation's best loved TV shows, such as Detective Inspector Tony Manning on ITV's *The Bay* and Dan Johnson on Sky's *Mount Pleasant.*

Theatre credits include: *Middle* and *Gethsemane* (National Theatre); *The Mouse and His Child* (RSC); *Inadmissible Evidence* (Donmar Warehouse); *Posh* (Royal Court Theatre); *The House They Grew Up In* (Chichester Festival) and *Glengarry Glen Ross* (West End).

TV credits include: *Crossfire, Four Lives, Just William* and *Death in Paradise* (BBC); *Litvinenko, Innocent, Vera, Doc Martin* and *Home Fires* (ITV) and *Cold Call* (Channel 5).

Film credits include: *The Government Inspector* (Channel 4); *Pirates of the Caribbean: Stranger Tides* (Walt Disney Pictures) and *Black Sea* (Universal Pictures).

CREATIVE TEAM

MICHAEL MORPURGO OBE | AUTHOR
Michael Morpurgo OBE is one of Britain's best loved writers for children, with sales of over 35 million copies. He has written over 150 books, has served as Children's Laureate and has won many prizes, including the Smarties Prize, the Writers Guild Award, the Whitbread Award, the Blue Peter Book Award and the Eleanor Farjeon Lifetime Achievement Award. With his wife, Clare, he is the co-founder of Farms for City Children. Michael was knighted in 2018 for services to literature and charity.

TATTY HENNESSY | PLAYWRIGHT
Tatty is a playwright, screenwriter and graduate of the Royal Court Playwrighting course and the Channel 4 Screenwriting Programme. Her play *A Hundred Words for Snow* was nominated for four Off West End Awards, has been translated into several languages and performed around the world. Other work includes: *Animal Farm* and *F Off* (National Youth Theatre); *Something Awful* (Vault Festival) and *a great big wooly mammoth thawing from the ice* (Burning Coal, North Carolina). She is a recipient of the Writers Guild of Great Britain New Play Commission scheme.

LUCY JANE ATKINSON | DIRECTOR
Lucy Jane Atkinson is an award-winning director of new writing. A graduate of LAMDA's Post Graduate Director's course and a member of the National Theatre's Directors course 2021. Her work focusses on new writing, and in 2018 she was named as number 1 on The Stage's Top Talents To Watch, which stated "her direction is acutely sensitive to the shifting energy of the writing. Evident but never overbearing."
Selected credits include: *Barriers* (National Theatre); *Girls & Boys* (Here For Now, Ontario); *A Great Big Wooly Mammoth Thawing From The Ice* and *I And You* (Burning Coal, North Carolina); *Testament* (Via Brooklyn, New York, Winner: BroadwayWorld Best Director 2022); *The Snow Queen* (Brighton Open Air Theatre); *Meat* (Theatre503); *Anguis, Phoenix, Joshua (& Me)* (Edinburgh Fringe); *A Hundred Words For Snow* (Trafalgar Studios, Winner: Offie Best Actress. Nominated: Offie Best Director, Best New Play); *Something Awful, Vespertilio, A Hundred Words For Snow, Cause, Secondbests* and *Testament* (VAULT Festival); *Oil And Matter* (Bunker Theatre) and *The Enchantment* (HERE Arts Centre, New York).
As Staff Director: *Middle* (National Theatre)

AMY BETHAN EVANS | DRAMATURG AND VISUALLY IMPAIRED CREATIVE CONSULTANT
Amy is a playwright, dramaturg and disability activist, originally from Bristol, where she instigated the new writing platforms at the Bierkeller. She has lived in London for five years, where her work includes: *Libby's Eyes* (Bunker Theatre) and *Tinted* (Edinburgh Fringe) which was shortlisted for the Birds-Of-Paradise Excellence in Theatre Award. Amy has mentored and facilitated workshops with Theatre 503 and Extant and is an alumnus of Graeae Write to Play, Soho Writers' Lab, English Touring Theatre's Nationwide Voices and BBC Writers' Access Room. She is currently on commission to the Royal Court and Bristol Old Vic, and on attachment at the National Theatre.

LOUISE WORRALL | DESIGN CONSULTANT
Louise Worrall is a performance designer based in Leyton, East London. Through collaboration with a myriad of artists and communities, Louise intends to create work that is relevant, thought-provoking and exciting. She is particularly interested in inclusive work that is both accessible for diverse audiences and for theatre-makers. Louise is excited by the prospect of enabling people who may not usually engage with performance projects and creating multi-sensory, memorable experiences that have a lasting legacy. Louise has a degree in Fine Art from Glasgow School of Art and an MA in Performance Design from Royal Welsh College of Music and Drama.
Credits include: Lead Designer for *Abundance* (an outdoor play space in Birmingham); Set & Costume Designer for *Anansi's Big Big Adventure* (Bristol Old Vic) and Design Assistant for Coventry City of Culture's Opening Event.

ALEX MUSGRAVE | LIGHTING DESIGNER
Alex was the recipient of the Association of Lighting Designers Lumiere Scheme and has been nominated for an Off West End Award for Best Lighting Design (*You Are Here*, Southwark Playhouse).
Design credits include: *Home* (Chichester Festival Theatre); *Tasting Notes*, *Anyone Can Whistle*, *You Are Here* and *Romeo and Juliet* (Southwark Playhouse); *Company* and *Oppenheimer* (Mountview); *13* and *Days of Significance* (ArtsEd); *Widows*, *Sweet Smell of Success* and *Bells are Ringing* (Guildford School of Acting).
Upcoming design credits include: *The Chronicles of Atom and Luna* (National Tour), *Tales of Acorn Wood* (National Tour) and *Alice in Wonderland* (Mountview).

XAVIER VELASTIN | SOUND DESIGNER
Xavier is a sound designer, composer and audio technologist who collaborates with theatres to develop innovative approaches to using sound onstage. His work ranges from immersive soundscapes to complex musical scores to precisely designed sound effects. Xavier also develops and produces his own performance work (usually about whales, for some reason) in close collaboration with other designers, performers and writers.

Offstage, Xavier has created sound installations, scored short films and designed sound for video games. In 2022, Xavier is co-delivering *Organism*, a project funded by Arts Council England, bringing together multidisciplinary artists in an online space to create a digital exhibition. Xavier's work has been presented at many established arts organisations such as the Barbican Centre, the Southbank Centre, The Place, the Royal Exchange Theatre, Leeds Playhouse, Cambridge Arts Centre, VAULT Festival and Homotopia Liverpool. He is a permanent resident of the Pervasive Media Studio in Watershed, Bristol.

DOUGLAS BAKER | CREATIVE CAPTIONS DESIGNER

Douglas is a disabled, multi-award nominated, interdisciplinary theatre director. He blends live performance with video and interactive animation under the name So It Goes. Douglas also works as a video and creative captions designer.
Credits include: *The Prince* by Abigail Thorn (Southwark Playhouse); *The Woman Who Amuses Herself*, *Holst: The Music in the Spheres* and *Ten Days in a Madhouse* (Jack Studio Theatre); *Faust* (Lazarus Theatre and Southwark Playhouse); *Moby Dick* (Jack Studio Theatre); *The Merry Wives of Windsor* and *Richard III* (Pendley Shakespeare Festival); *Castles Palaces Castles* (Prague Quadrennial) and *Dante's Divine Comedy* (Barons Court Theatre).

SAMUEL BREWER | AUDIO DESCRIPTION CONSULTANT

Samuel is an actor and theatre-maker who graduated from BA Acting CDT at The Royal Central School of Speech and Drama in 2020. He is co-founder of FlawBored theatre company, winners of the Les Enfants Terribles x Greenwich Theatre Award for their upcoming debut show. As an actor and theatre-maker, he has worked with numerous companies including the Barbican, Asylum Arts, Complicité and The Watermill Theatre.
He is also an ambassador for the Disability Artist Network Collective. He runs workshops focusing on access tools in the rehearsal room – skill-building with practitioners to make their methodologies more accessible. These workshops are designed to be active, engaging and cheeky. Samuel describes the way he works as "take the work seriously, don't take yourself seriously."

THE SLEEPING SWORD was first produced at The Watermill Theatre between Thursday 27 October and Saturday 5 November 2022 The cast was as follows:

BUN .... Aarian Mehrabani
ANNA.......... Tika Mu'tamir
VIV .... Kirsty Ferriggi
AUDIOBOOK NARRATOR .... Daniel Ryan

PLAYWRIGHT .... Tatty Hennessy
DIRECTOR .... Lucy Jane Atkinson
DRAMATURG AND VISUALLY IMPAIRED CREATIVE CONSULTANT .... Amy Bethan Evans
DESIGN CONSULTANT .... Louise Worrall
LIGHTING DESIGNER .... Alex Musgrave
SOUND DESIGNER .... Xavier Velastin
CREATIVE CAPTIONS DESIGNER.......... Douglas Baker
AUDIO DESCRIPTION CONSULTANT .... Samuel Brewer

PRODUCER .... Lucy Rahim
TOUR PRODUCTION MANAGERS .... Matt Britton and Alice Reddick
COMPANY STAGE MANAGER.......... Emily Stedman
WATERMILL STAGE MANAGER .... Cat Pewsey
HEAD OF WARDROBE .... Emily Barratt
THEATRE TECHNICIANS .... Thom Townsend, Chris Parker
DEPUTY STAGE MANGER .... Caitlin Ravenscroft
ASSISTANT STAGE MANAGER .... Amelia Costello
ACCESS SUPPORT WORKER.......... Chloe Palmer
REHEARSAL AND PRODUCTION PHOTOGRAPHER.......... Mark Senior

With thanks to:
Tracy Fletcher at Mary Hare School, Newbury, the Royal National Institute for the Blind (RNIB), Chaddleworth St Andrew's & Shefford CE Federated Primary Schools and Mark Bothwick at Bryher Sound Recording Workshop.

CHARACTERS

VIV
BUN
ANNA
LUKE
DAD
MRS PARSONS
SIR BEDEVERE
KING ARTHUR
MORGANA LE FEY
HIPPY DUDE

NOTES ON THE PLAY

The audio description for The Watermill production is integrated into this script. If you need to make adjustments to the text so that it better describes your production, please go ahead.

NOTES ON CHARACTERS

These are to be split between a cast of three, including at least two visually impaired actors.
You cannot perform this play with sighted actors pretending to be visually impaired.

In The Watermill production, lines in this text were amended to give Mrs Parsons and Bun visual impairments that more closely reflected those of the actors playing them. Future productions are warmly welcomed to do the same.

NOTES ON SOUND EFFECTS

In The Watermill Theatre's production, the characters use a wide range of objects to make sounds in front of a microphone, creating some of the environments and sound effects live. Here are some of the sounds they discovered:

• Gusts of wind: An old leather jacket held out in front and then flapped around in an irregular fashion.
• Boat flagpoles gently knocking against each other as they move on the water: Two short aluminium poles lightly touching each other and ringing out.
• Water sloshing around a wooden dock: Two plastic bottles without their lids being moved around in a tub of water.
• Waves crashing onto rocks: One person emptying a small bucket of water into a tub of water (creating the wave crash), with another person moving pebbles in a wave motion to create the sound of the water receding over rocks or a pebble beach.
• Boat ropes stretching on a harbour: a leather belt twisted around a few times then squeezed and released.

PLAYWRIGHT'S NOTE

This play was over two years in the making, and could not exist at all without the sensitive, playful and generous work of an awful lot of people.

I am utterly indebted to the careful and rigorous dramaturgy of Amy Bethan Evans, whose knowledge of Arthurian legend and willingness to cancel me were both invaluable. Not only is the play a better play, but I think I'm a better artist for our time together.

This script was made what it is through a research and development process involving Samuel Brewer, Ben Wilson, Georgie Morrell and Tika Mu'tamir; you couldn't ask for a better round table. Much of what was said is unrepeatable; but all of it was illuminating. Their fingerprints are all over this play, and it is better, richer, more nuanced, stranger, sadder, funnier and more truthful because of them. It was a galvanising week, inspiring us to dream bigger about the ways access and collaboration could influence the form of the story, and the process of staging it. We wanted the creation of this show to enact the principals of the show. I hope we've succeeded.

I'm deeply grateful to The Watermill Theatre, firstly for entrusting me with this commission and continuing to support its development throughout the pandemic. Walking around Victoria Park with a cassette player, listening to Morpurgo read to me about King Arthur, kept me a particular sort of sane in a difficult time. Secondly, I am grateful to them for their spirit and openness, for throwing themselves behind the way we wanted to work and what we wanted to achieve, especially when that was difficult. I am so glad this was the sword's first home.

Our premiere cast, Tika Mu'tamir, Aarian Mehrabani and Kirsty Ferriggi, were smart, irreverent, playful brave magicians. It's a privilege to have my words brought to life with their skills. We auditioned a wide range of utterly wonderful people for this production, it felt criminal we could only cast three of them, so I would also like to thank everyone who gave their time and put themselves through a dreaded Zoom audition to meet with us.

We were brilliantly lucky to have Xavier Velastin and his big yellow suitcase of foley tricks to bring the sound world of this play alive. He's a bit of a mad genius. Louise Worrall created a set in which every element had to do about three things at a time, while fitting in a van to be reassembled in a school hall. Thanks as well to Samuel Brewer and Douglas Baker who innovatively and creatively supported our ambition to make every single performance of this show an accessible performance through integrated audio description and creative captioning.

For a brave and careful custodian of the text, you can't do much better than my long-suffering collaborator, director Lucy Jane Atkinson. So far, I've forced her to figure out how to fly a helicopter, skin a deer and capsize a fishing boat, and those are only the onstage ways that I've made her life difficult. I am, as always, grateful to entrust her with my words.

I'd also love to thank Michael Morpurgo for his extraordinary generosity with his story. *The Sleeping Sword* is, among other things, about the power of stories to show us new ways of living, to make us feel brave, to rethink what we thought we knew and empower us to make our lives bigger. Bun tells a story to change his world. You couldn't ask for much better inspiration than that.

Tatty Hennessy

DIRECTOR'S NOTE

I grew up obsessed with Michael Morpurgo. I would read and re-read my copies of *The Ghost of Grania O'Malley*, *The King In The Forest* and *The Wreck of the Zanzibar* until the pages fell out. I loved his sense of adventure and the kindness, bravery and ingenuity of his characters, but most of all, I loved the fact that his stories don't talk down to the reader. Morpurgo treats children as fully formed people with complex, difficult, confusing and exciting lives of their own. I also love how storytelling is such an important part of his characters' lives, how they use stories to understand and process their experiences and make their worlds better.

In developing this adaptation, our mission was to stay true to that spirit. To treat our audiences with respect as we lead them through the highs and lows of Bun's story, as he learns to live with and embrace his blindness. During our workshops last year, and in rehearsal, our cast and company have been incredibly generous in sharing their own experiences of blindness and visual impairment. In doing so they have provided us with valuable insight into a wide variety of visually impaired experiences. This has allowed us to create a show which feels at once faithful to Morpurgo's original novel while also reflecting contemporary conversations around blindness and visual impairment, which have changed a lot since the novel's original publication.

As a director, so much of your job is visual; you tell stories through pictures, tableau and blocking. The most challenging and exciting aspect of directing this piece has been thinking about staging a play in which sight is not the most important thing. Like the characters in the play, we've had to figure out new methods of storytelling. I've been lucky enough to work with an incredibly talented, playful and curious group of cast and creatives willing to think outside the box and find innovative, imaginative ways to make a show that is equally exciting whether you can see it or not.

My hope is that this show inspires a new generation of theatre-makers to think about integrated access not as a burden or a problem to overcome, but as an opportunity for theatrical innovation. Storytelling is an inherent part of being human, and theatre is the oldest medium we have for telling stories. It is our responsibility as theatre-makers to find ways to make sure the stories we tell are as accessible as possible to anyone who wants to hear them.

Lucy Jane Atkinson

'A tiny Berkshire village producing world-class theatre' – *BBC South*

There has always been a water mill in Bagnor. Its existence was first recorded in the Doomsday Book. Over time, it has served as a corn mill, paper mill and fuller mill – if you come to the theatre, you can still see the original wheel!

In the early 1960s, the mill was bought by David and Judy Gollins, originally intending that it would become a cathedral, before David changed his mind and turned it into the beautiful intimate theatre we have today (though the seats did come from Winchester Cathedral).

The Watermill's first professional season opened in 1967, with local actors performing two plays in the summer. Since then, it has produced award-winning work that has been recognised throughout the UK and abroad. We are a regional powerhouse, consistently making an innovative contribution to the vibrant and diverse landscape of UK theatre, reaching far beyond our auditorium's 220 seats.

The very best artists and creative teams – both established and in the early stages of their careers – are our lifeblood, earning The Watermill a reputation as one of the best producing theatres in the country. We continually aim to present a programme of inspiring and thought-provoking live performances and outreach opportunities that have lasting impact. Our artistic ambition is clear in our range of work, from new writing and musicals to Shakespeare and classic plays. Our pioneering approach has made us renowned for our actor-musician productions, which bring new dimensions to well-known titles and new writing: The Watermill's actor-musician production of Andrew Lloyd Webber's *Whistle Down the Wind* in 2022 was nominated for the UK Theatre Best Musical award, and our 2019 production of *Amélie* embarked on a UK tour before taking up West End residence at The Other Palace and picking up nominations for three Olivier awards and a GRAMMY.

Alongside our shows on The Watermill stage, we enjoy touring work around the country to a wide range of communities. We have secured numerous West End and national transfers, as well as touring internationally to places such as Nepal, New York, Bombay and Barbados. As part of our commitment to the community, every year we take a show to local villages, providing access to professional theatre in rural areas. We also visit schools, taking scaled-down, vibrant new adaptations of classic texts — like *The Sleeping Sword* — into classrooms to support students' learning. We believe that everyone deserves access to a rich education and the chance to participate in top-quality theatre, and we work with around 19,000 people every year at The Watermill and in the wider community.

We would love to welcome you to The Watermill soon! For more information about our upcoming productions, please visit our website or social media pages: watermill.org.uk

"What a location! Forget the glitz of the West End: try walking up a country lane, past waddling ducks, to this lovely little theatre in a converted mill." – *The Mail on Sunday*

Artistic Director: Paul Hart
Executive Director: Claire Murray

PROLOGUE

(We hear the overblown, exciting music of a 90s audiobook. Trumpets, drums, the works. Sound effects of a baying crowd, the sound of metal on stone etc...)

AUDIOBOOK. "Whosoever pulls this sword from the stone is the rightful King of Britain!" The Kingdom of Britain was in darkness. War and famine ravaged the land, families divided. The people were desperate for a leader to guide them, but nobody could decide who that leader should be.

And so they turned to the great wise wizard Merlin for aid, and Merlin devised a test. He summoned all the knights and squires of the realm to the great castle courtyard, and there he took a shining sword and plunged the blade deep into a great rock.

"Whosoever pulls this sword from the stone is the rightful King of Britain!" he declared.

BUN. This is my favourite book of all time. *The Legend of King Arthur.*

AUDIOBOOK. A great crowd gathered. Every man wanted to be the chosen one, the man destined for power.

BUN. Some of you might know the story already? About the sword in the stone? Yeah? It's pretty famous. Merlin's set this test, yeah, to see who should be king of England. Pull the sword out of the stone and boom. Crown, sceptre, castle. Done. And all these massive knights line up and try it...

AUDIOBOOK. One by one the men approached and gripped the golden hilt. One by one they heaved, but not a single one could move the sword an inch.

BUN. But then.

AUDIOBOOK. A boy stepped forward.

BUN. This kid steps up.

AUDIOBOOK. He was small and slight, still a child. A stable boy, no more. The crowd laughed.

BUN. They all laugh at him.

AUDIOBOOK. "Look at that welp! Him, King of England!"

BUN. But Merlin shuts them up.

AUDIOBOOK. "Let him try." Merlin said.

BUN. So he does.

AUDIOBOOK. The boy approached the sword. He reached out his hand.

AUDIOBOOK & BUN. The hilt fit his fingers as if it had been built for him.

BUN. I like that bit.

AUDIOBOOK. A hush fell.

BUN. Sssh.

AUDIOBOOK. And he pulled. The sword slipped through the rock easily, as if the stone were butter. He turned and brandished the blade above his head.

BUN. He's done it!

AUDIOBOOK. A gasp echoed across the courtyard. Merlin spoke;

"This boy before you is Arthur Pendragon, the rightful King of Britain. Destined for greatness. He is your one true king!"

(The crowd roars. **BUN** *makes crowd noises.)*

BUN. All hail King Arthur! Oh, uh, Hi. I'm Ben, by the way. Ben Bundle. But everyone calls me Bun, for short. I'm... *(The actor playing* **BUN** *describes themselves.)* And I'm blind. And right now you're here with me, in my bedroom *(The actor playing* **BUN** *describes the set for us.)* We're listening to my favourite book and also the absolute number one best book of all time, *The Legend of King Arthur.*

AUDIOBOOK. And so Arthur was crowned King, and went with all his knights to Camelot, to rule over the Kingdom of Britain and bring her back to glory.

BUN. And that's just like, Chapter *One.* There's so much stuff that happens. Battles and dragons and magic. Arthur lives in this huge castle called Camelot with all his mates who are knights, right, like Lancelot, and Bedevere, and they go on adventures and quests. And he's best mates with an actual *wizard* called Merlin and Merlin is super powerful and he can fly and shapeshift and see the future. Oh OK there's this one bit, right, where a guy's head gets chopped off and he just picks it up and carries it away under his arm like it's a football. And there's another bit where a guy makes a coat out of people's faces. And there's another bit where a guy stabs a dragon-man right in the mouth like – aaaaghgghh!!

*(***BUN** *stabs a dragon-man right in the mouth.)*

But mostly it's about Arthur, becoming king, fulfilling his destiny. It's mint. I used to read the book so much the pages were falling out. Then when I had my accident and lost my sight my friend Anna got me an audiobook of it, and a tape player. Here –

*(***BUN** *shows us the tape player, describes it to us, and talks us through the noises it can make. Oooo.)*

We looked everywhere for a download but it's such an old book they didn't have it, we could only find it on this weird old thing called a *cassette*. Here, listen

*(***BUN** *holds up the tape and presses play and we hear, through its tinny speakers a version of the music we just heard.)*

It's pretty ancient *but* it's great, I can listen to *The Legend of King Arthur*, every day whenever I like. And that got me thinking. Maybe I could even record my *own* tape. My own legend, about everything that happened to me. The Legend of Ben Bundle. So yeah. That's what we're here to do, right now.

*(***ANNA** *coughs.)*

Oh, right. I'm not doing it alone. My friends Anna and Viv are here helping me.

ANNA. Alright? This is Anna.

VIV. And hello! I'm Viv.

BUN. We're gonna make the number two absolute best audiobook of all time, it's gonna have fights and magic and music and sound effects and everything. Anna and Viv are gonna play themselves, and the other characters, and help me make the sounds. This is Anna

ANNA. Hi, I'm Anna, I'm Bun's friend, I'm much cooler than him.

BUN. Hey, do it properly.

ANNA. I am!

BUN. Like we / practised it.

ANNA. Fine OK, hi, I'm Anna, I'm eleven, *(***ANNA** *describes herself.)*

BUN. Say who you're / being

ANNA. What?

BUN. Say who you're being in the play.

ANNA. I'm being myself, Anna.

BUN. Great, OK, and this is Viv.

VIV. Hello, I'm Viv. (**VIV** *describes herself.*) I'm visually impaired. I'm going to be performing myself and, well, everybody else. Shall I say who?

BUN. Let's tell them as we go, no spoilers.

ANNA. Wait, she gets to play more characters than me?

BUN. Yes.

ANNA. That's unfair.

BUN. She's reliable.

ANNA. That's fair.

BUN. I've never made an audiobook before but I've listened to loads of them so how hard can it be? The best ones have sound effects, so we've got to have those. We've got some stuff here we're gonna use to make noises.

> (**BUN**, **ANNA** *and* **VIV** *talk us through the set and props that make noises, and what noises they might make. Maybe there's a loop pedal and they explain that. Sometimes they enlist the audience, teaching us sounds that we'll be called upon to make later. It's super exciting. We're having a lot of fun.*)

VIV. I think we have everything we need, Bun. Shall we start?

BUN. Yeah. Yeah I guess we should. OK. This is my story. It's called *The Sleeping Sword*. It's about what happened to me. My accident, losing my sight, and everything that happened after.

It's about a boy.

ANNA. And a girl.

BUN. And a girl, and a sword, and an adventure at sea. It's about magic, mystery, hope, triumph and disaster. There's danger, despair and a happy ending. And it's all true. Well. Mostly.

So. Here we go. Are you ready?

ANNA. Absolutely.

VIV. Ready.

BUN. And you out there, are you ready?

(We're ready.)

OK, here goes. Quiet please. Recording in 3, 2, 1...

*(**BUN** presses record.)*

The Sleeping Sword. Side One. Chapter 1. The Island.

Scene One

(We hear the sounds of a busy day down by the harbour, and we find ourselves on the island of Bryher.)

BUN. I live on a tiny little island way off the coast of Cornwall called Bryher. We're thirty miles away from the mainland and we're too small for planes so the only way here is by boat, over the sea. The nearest school's on the next island over, so me and my friends get the boat to school every day. It's class. See, Bryher is the best place in the world. It's so small that wherever you go you can hear the ocean. You can walk round the whole island in one afternoon. We've got all kinds of birds, plovers and oystercatchers and linnets. Sometimes there's dolphins in the cove.

(**ANNA** *does a rubbish dolphin noise.)*

What is that?

ANNA. It's a dolphin.

BUN. It's rubbish.

ANNA. What, you could do better?

VIV. How's this?

(**VIV** *does a brilliant dolphin noise.)*

BUN. Brilliant.

There's beaches and cliffs, Hell Bay where the waves CRASH on the rocks, and little islands out in the ocean that only appear when the tide is low, like magic. And every summer, on the summer solstice, that's the longest day of the year, there's a huge party on the beach to watch the sun go down, with fires and sea shanties.

(They sing;)

PULL FOR THE SHORE, SAILOR, PULL FOR THE SHORE!
HEED NOT THE ROLLING WAVES, BUT BEND TO THE OAR;
SAFE IN THE LIFE BOAT, SAILOR, CLING TO SELF NO MORE!
LEAVE THE POOR OLD STRANDED WRECK,
AND PULL FOR THE SHORE!

Not bad. I live with my Dad. (Viv, you're playing him!)

DAD. Come on Bun, the tide waits for no man

BUN. He's a fisherman. Some days I go out on the boat with him to help haul in the lobster pots. I've got my own one with my name on it!

DAD. Heave! What a catch, lad!

BUN. He says I'm his lucky charm because he always catches more when I'm with him. I love going out on the waves, smelling the salt and feeling the boat go up and down like a rollercoaster. If you look at the horizon, you don't get seasick. Hard to starboard!

DAD. Aye aye, Captain!

BUN. But most of the time I'm just mucking about with my best friend, Luke. (That's you again, Viv)

LUKE. Come on, race you!

BUN. And his big sister, Anna.

ANNA. Hurry up shrimpy, last one there buys the chips!

BUN. The whole island's ours to do what we like. We can climb up Hell Bay in a storm and scream out over the ocean.

ANNA, LUKE & BUN. *1, 2, 3, AAAHHHH!!*

BUN. We can bury each other in the sand.

(**LUKE** *No no no the waves are coming aggh!*)

We can throw chips to the seagulls.

(**ANNA** *Oh my god that's one's giant!!*)

We can laugh at Mr Jenkins wearing his Speedos at Fraggles' café. Snorkel in the kelp beds. Give tourists fake directions.

ANNA. Yeah it's just at the top of that really steep hill, keep climbing.

TOURIST. You're sure?

BUN. A hundred percent.

TOURIST. Thanks!

BUN. We can find crabs in the rockpools or chuck seaweed about. The summer holidays are the best, when we can do anything we like, when the whole island's our kingdom and everyday is full of adventure. Running down the grassy hill from our farm through town, down the muddy path through the fields to where the real road starts, past Luke and Anna's house, past the tuck shop, along the harbour where the fishermen shout and seagulls shriek, along the rickety old wooden jetty and then JUMP somersault into the ocean.

SPLASH.

(*Silence.*)

That's what we were doing. The day I lost my sight.

It started normal. I was in my room, reading *The Legend of King Arthur.* I'd started again from the beginning for the millionth time and was up to this super cool bit where King Arthur fights this mysterious masked soldier.

(*Reading.*) "The masked soldier lunged at Arthur, bringing his sword crashing down. Arthur staggered back and fell to the dust..."

Didn't I tell you the battles were class?

(Reading.) "He bore down on Arthur, who thrust up his sword with all his might and watched in horror as it shattered against the masked soldier's armour, breaking into a thousand pieces and leaving him defenceless. Arthur looked up his enemy's face, hidden in the visor. The knight raised his weapon to deliver the death blow.

"You fool!" Arthur cried. "I am your King!"

ANNA. Alright shrimpy!

BUN. But I was *rudely* interrupted by Anna and Luke. Hey, give me my book back!

LUKE. We're going to jump off the jetty, you coming?

BUN. I'm reading.

ANNA. You've read this book like a million times.

BUN. Yeah, and I'd like to read it a million and one times.

LUKE. But we're gonna jump off the jetty!

ANNA. And they're decorating the harbour for the solstice festival next weekend, putting a bandstand up and everything.

BUN. Boring.

ANNA. It's a special one this year, right, OK, this year the solstice is on the same day as a full moon, and that hasn't happened / in.

BUN. Booooooring.

ANNA. It hasn't happened in hundreds of years! I bet it's gonna make the tides go *crazy*.

LUKE. I don't care about the solstice I just wanna go swimming.

ANNA. Classic Pisces.

LUKE. It's *baking*, come on. We can get chips at Fraggles on the way.

BUN. I don't feel like it.

LUKE. Why not?

BUN. I just don't.

ANNA. Oooh, I get it.

BUN. What?

ANNA. you're scared.

BUN. Scared?

ANNA. Of jumping off the jetty. You're scared of heights.

BUN. I'm not scared of heights.

ANNA. Don't worry you'll grow out of it it's common in children.

BUN. Luke, tell her.

LUKE. You haven't jumped the jetty in a while, Bun.

BUN. Who's side are you on?

LUKE. Last time you said it was too windy and the time before that you saw that weird fish.

BUN. Well there was a weird fish.

ANNA. It's OK Bun, we get it. If you'd rather stay here reading about other people doing brave things than doing brave things...

BUN. That's not true!

ANNA. Prove it.

BUN. Fine. Last one there buys the chips. Deal?

ANNA. Deal.

BUN. Let's go!

(**BUN** *runs.*)

LUKE. Wait!

BUN. I ran down the stairs, slamming the door behind me. Out the front door and down path through the field to where the real road starts, past Anna and Luke's house and the tuck shop, past the fishermen shouting and the seagulls shrieking, towards the rickety jetty, past the bandstand for the solstice. The men waved as I whooshed by. I could hear Luke and Anna behind me.

LUKE. *Bun wait!* **ANNA.** *Bun! Stop! STOP!*

BUN. I kept running. I wasn't going to stop. I sprinted full pelt and I jumped off the jetty, I leapt I FLEW, I tucked my feet in close and I span into a perfect, textbook, Olympic-level.

DOUBLE BACKFLIIIP!

(He makes the sound of applause.)

And then I realised it was taking a lot longer than usual to hit the water.

SMACK.

(Smack.)

Everything went dark.

(The sound of the ocean becomes the sound of a hospital.)

Scene Two

(**BUN** *wakes up.*)

BUN. When I woke up, I knew I was in a hospital because I could smell it. I remembered the smell from visiting Gran. Was I visiting Gran? I couldn't remember. I was lying in a bed. And I couldn't see anything.

A thing a lot of people don't know about blindness is everybody has it different. Some of us still see at the edges, just with a black or blurry spot in the middle. For some people it's the other way around. For some of us everything is cloudy. Some of us see shapes and colours, or different coloured lights. Some of us see patterns, or even hallucinations. My blindness means I see mostly darkness, sometimes a bit of light and shade. But it's different for different people. I didn't know that, then, when I woke up in hospital. All I knew then was that I couldn't see anything. It was just dark. Like I had a bandage on my face. I reached my hand out but the air was empty.

Dad? Hello?

This bit's kind of rough. But it's important for the story. And like I said, there's a happy ending.

DAD. Bun! You're up.

BUN. Dad?

DAD. How are you feeling, lad?

BUN. What's going on? Where am I?

DAD. You're fine, you're in hospital.

BUN. What happened? I was on the jetty...

DAD. You had a bit of a fall, that's all.

BUN. I remember I was running, and then I jumped and...

DAD. The tide was lower than usual, the sea was out, it was out too low, you hit your head on the rocks. You need water to jump into, silly, don't you know that?

BUN. I can't see.

(Beat.)

Have they put something in my eyes? Dad?

(Beat.)

Dad?

DAD. They've done a lot of scans.

BUN. Scans?

DAD. It's from the bump on your head.

BUN. What is? Dad? Tell me.

DAD. It's. Your vision... something from the crack to your head. It. Your sight. Your sight's gone.

BUN. What does that mean?

DAD. You know / what I mean, Bun.

BUN. Dad tell me.

DAD. They think you're blind, Bun.

(Beat.)

BUN. What?

DAD. When you hit your head... it was a nasty knock, they think it, it did something to your brain.

BUN. What like... forever?

DAD. Yes.

BUN. But... it was just an accident. It was just a stupid accident, I was just running and I jumped and then...

DAD. Ssh, I know.

BUN. They'll fix it. They'll fix it. Right?

DAD. They. They say they can't.

BUN. What do you mean, they can't? You said they did a scan, they'll find the problem, they'll fix it.

DAD. They can't. I'm sorry.

BUN. But... why?

DAD. Listen hey, we're alright, eh? We're alright. No sense getting all upset. Someone's going to come and visit, talk you through... everything. Get you back up and running, back to normal.

BUN. Normal?

DAD. You'll be back out on the boat in no time, eh? My lucky charm. It will all be fine, Bun. It will all be absolutely fine.

BUN. After a couple of days they let him take me home. It was a long way to go. There's no hospital on Bryher so we'd had to go all the way to the mainland. It's thirty miles on a boat and the waves were awful, Dad's boat going up and down like a rollercoaster, but without the horizon to look at I felt sicker and sicker. I lay down on the floor and held on tight.

DAD. Here, Bun, grab the wheel we'll steer together.

BUN. No.

DAD. Come on, Captain, take us starboard.

BUN. I feel sick.

DAD. A fisherman's son seasick? Can't be having that. Try it. Here.

BUN. No.

DAD. You'll feel better.

BUN. No I won't. Stop.

DAD. Bun. Come on, get up, it helps to... to stand up.

BUN. But it didn't anymore. Everything was strange. We stepped off the boat onto the rickety, creaky, swaying jetty. The fishermen were shouting and the seagulls were shrieking. There was music...

(Throw out the lifeline! Throw out the lifeline!)

(Someone is drifting away!)

I couldn't tell where all the noise was coming from so it was all confusing and scary. Dad led me back up the past the tuck shop, past Luke and Anna's house. They didn't come out to meet me.

DAD. Here we are. Home sweet home.

BUN. Dad took me to my room. And he kept on saying, over and over.

DAD. Not to worry, Bun. It will all be fine.

BUN. No it won't stop it, stop saying that!

DAD. Bun...

BUN. Obviously its not fine, obviously it's not going to be fine! Just. Leave me alone!

(A door slams.)

It was quiet in my room. I tried screwing my eyes up tight and opening them. Nothing. Just. Black.

I didn't know where things were, which way I was facing.

I put my hand out and I felt... my book. *The Legend of King Arthur.* Where Anna must have left it when we ran to the jetty. I picked it up.

I could feel the pages flick across my thumb. I could picture the cover in my head. I could feel the folded edge of the page I was reading when Anna interrupted me. I knew the words were in there.

Arthur was fighting the masked soldier. He was losing. His sword was broken. "Arthur watched as it shattered against his foe's armour, breaking into a thousand pieces." He... he looks up... he says... he...

I couldn't remember. And before I knew what I was doing... I was ripping out the pages.

*(**BUN** rips at the book.)*

Ripping and ripping.

Why? Why me? This isn't *fair.*

I thought I was never gonna read again. Never go on the boat with Dad again. Not be his lucky charm, not run round the island, dive and somersault. Never be free again.

Obviously *now* I know that's not true. But back then, I didn't. Back then, that's what I believed.

This bit's really tough. I was really sad so the story gets sad for a while. But it's important. And I promise it turns out OK.

(Music.)

After I'd ripped out every last page, I didn't feel angry anymore. I just felt. Numb. And alone.

I stayed very very quiet and I waited to hear Dad to come up to bed. It's actually a myth that blind people have super hearing which is annoying cos it would've been useful. After I heard him come up, I waited a bit more, just to be safe. I couldn't look at my phone to see the time so I counted my heartbeats. Nine hundred and ninety nine. One thousand.

I felt for the doorhandle...

(**BUN** *finds the doorhandle.)*

And crept out into the hallway. I knew the stairs were to my left. I held the banister and slowly, slowly, made my way downstairs. The front door was just across the kitchen. Quietly, don't wake him up…

I tripped.

One of Dad's slippers. He was always leaving them out. I held it for a moment…

Keep going. I could feel the coats along the wall, the doormat under my feet. I found the door handle, turned the latch…

(**BUN** *opens the door.)*

The air outside was cold. Normally the island seems tiny, but at that moment, it felt giant. Bryher's full of hills and cliffs. Hell Bay was the closest. The drop was steep. The rocks sharp underneath. I was going to jump.

It's sort of hard to talk about it now because of how sad I was. But I think I need to talk about it. I think it helps.

(Maybe we hear a snatch of **[BRIGHTLY BEAMS OUR FATHER'S MERCY]** *or* **[HOME FROM THE SEA]**.*)*

The road up there was tricky even if you could see it. I fell a few times. I knew if I kept the hedges to my right and kept following the path up I'd make it. A blast of wind in my face told me I was at the top. The sea sounded fierce below. I wondered if the sunrise was starting, if there were dolphins in the water, watching. I could feel the rocks under me tremble when the waves hit. They must be vicious, the waves. I realised I wasn't going to get to go to the solstice festival.

I didn't want to do it. But I didn't know what to do.

I took a step closer. And another. And another...

ANNA. Come back Bun. You're too close.

BUN. It was Anna.

ANNA. Get away from the edge.

BUN. She took my hand. And I stepped back from the cliff. And I hugged her.

ANNA. It's freezing up here, Bun. Let's get inside.

Scene Three

BUN. She led me along the path and we crept back to my room and sat on my bed. I asked her

(To **ANNA.***)* How did you find me?

ANNA. I was looking through my telescope, out my window at the moon. It was like, huge and orange tonight. The tides have been so crazy and with the full moon coming up on the same night as the solstice I wanted to write it all down in my star journal and… that's when I saw you. And I couldn't figure out what you were doing so I thought maybe you were sleepwalking, like maybe the bump to your head had… and I thought here we go, he's gonna go getting himself in trouble but also I know you're not supposed to wake up sleepwalking people so I just thought I'd follow you, make sure you were OK. And then. Then I saw what you were doing.

(Beat.)

How's your head?

BUN. Super.

ANNA. You got a big scar?

BUN. Feels big.

ANNA. Let's see.

BUN. Here, I'll show you.

ANNA. Cool. I heard about… your eyes.

BUN. It's my brain, not my eyes. My eyes work fine just my brain won't listen to them.

ANNA. Right. Sorry.

BUN. Why you sorry, you didn't do it.

ANNA. Do you remember going in the helicopter?

BUN. No.

ANNA. It landed right on the beach like in a movie. I took a photo, look… Sorry. They put you on this stretcher and tied you down so your head wouldn't move. It was so cool.

BUN. Who called the ambulance?

ANNA. Luke.

BUN. I don't remember anything. Did I say anything?

ANNA. You were *out*. I thought you were dead at first. You were so cold and kind of floppy?

BUN. You touched me?

ANNA. Only when I gave you CPR.

BUN. You *kissed* me?!

ANNA. No, I gave you CPR.

BUN. That's / disgusting.

ANNA. I wasn't happy about / it either.

BUN. Talk about kicking a man when he's down.

ANNA. Yeah well you had bad breath, so.

BUN. Did not.

ANNA. Did too, like old eggs. I nearly passed out. It was a nasty fall, Bun.

BUN. Nailed the double backflip, though.

ANNA. The paramedics said you were lucky to be alive.

BUN. Yeah well. I don't feel very lucky. *(Beat.)* Luke never came to visit.

ANNA. I don't think he knows what to say.

(Beat.)

What happened here? I mean, with the book. It's all ripped up.

BUN. Yeah.

ANNA. It's the one you love, what happened?

BUN. Don't need it now, do I?

ANNA. I could read it to you?

BUN. Why would you do that?

ANNA. I dunno, might be nice.

BUN. Like a baby?

ANNA. No, just.

BUN. Why are you being nice to me?

ANNA. What's wrong with being nice to you?

BUN. You're never nice to me, why are you being nice?

ANNA. Because.../ I ...

BUN. Because you feel sorry for me?

ANNA. Maybe a little.

BUN. Well don't.

ANNA. Bun...

BUN. Just. Go home.

ANNA. What, so you can go for another walk up the cliff again? Not likely.

BUN. I don't *want* you to feel sorry for me.

ANNA. OK, so I won't, look, I'm trying, ok, this is / new for me too.

BUN. Wow here's your medal, such an amazing person, how do you / do it.

ANNA. I want to get it right, I want to learn.

BUN. I *hate* that I have to teach you. I hate it. I just want to go back to how I was, I want to be normal.

ANNA. Alright, settle down Shrimpy, you were never normal.

(Beat. **BUN** *laughs.* **ANNA** *laughs too.)*

BUN. Says the girl with a star journal.

ANNA. Classic Capricorn. What's so great about this book, then?

BUN. You never read it?

ANNA. Just a load of moody boys waving swords about, isn't it?

BUN. There's girls in it too. Arthur's enemy, Morgana le Fey, she's a girl.

ANNA. Is she a knight?

BUN. She's an evil sorceress who wants to kill Arthur and claim the kingdom for herself.

ANNA. She sounds mint.

BUN. She's literally evil!

ANNA. Like what?

BUN. Like... OK, the bit I'm up to right now. Arthur's fighting this mega battle against a mysterious masked knight. And he's being totally overpowered. Like, his sword shatters into loads of tiny pieces and he's about to be stabbed.

ANNA. OK maybe this is interesting.

BUN. Just wait. Cause then the other knight takes off his helmet and Arthur sees his face and *plot twist,* it's his *best friend,* Sir Bedevere!

ANNA. His best friend tries to kill him? Why?

BUN. Because of Morgana le Fey! She kidnapped him, cast an evil spell on him, and sent him to kill his own king!

ANNA. What happens next?

BUN. Arthur breaks the spell and they escape together. And Bedevere spends the rest of his life by Arthur's side, defending him against Morgana.

ANNA. Guess he must've felt pretty guilty.

BUN. Yeah. Anyway that's what I was reading the day of the accident, before…

(Beat.)

ANNA. Yeah… hey, what if I find you an audiobook of this? That way you can listen to it whenever you want, without anyone having to help you.

BUN. An audiobook?

ANNA. Yeah. And I promise this isn't me being nice or feeling sorry for you because I'm not doing it for free. You have to do something for me, too.

BUN. OK, what?

ANNA. You have to promise me that if you ever feel like… Like sleepwalking up to the cliff again. You'll talk to me first. So I can wake you up. Deal?

BUN. Deal. What are you doing?

ANNA. I was gonna shake your hand.

BUN. OK, just tell me first.

ANNA. OK. Shall we shake on it?

BUN. OK. There.

(They shake hands, the seriousness makes them laugh.)

Maybe… you could read a bit of it now. If you wanted.

ANNA. Yeah? OK. Where were you up to?

BUN. So OK, Arthur broke his sword when he fought with Bedevere, so he has to get a new one. So Merlin takes him to meet with Lady Vivian.

ANNA. Lady Vivian?

BUN. Yeah, see, that's another girl!

ANNA. And is she terrible and evil too?

BUN. No, she's good, she's the Lady of the Lake, an elven queen of water magic. She gives him his new sword, Excalibur.

ANNA. I've heard of Excalibur!

BUN. It's a magic sword, forged in elven fires.

ANNA. The pages are everywhere...

BUN. There should be a drawing of Arthur in a boat on the water. That's basically where I was up to.

ANNA. Oh yeah, here's the page. Ummm... *(Reads.)* "Lady Vivian held out the sword, Excalibur, and Arthur took it.

"This is Excalibur, the ancient blade forged in elven fires. It has lain here, sleeping at the bottom of the lake, for thousands of years, waiting for you."

Arthur took hold of the shining hilt, and felt a great power coursing through him.

Then Merlin spoke. *(**ANNA** puts on a silly voice.)* "With this sword, Arthur, nothing can harm you."

BUN. That's not what Merlin sounds like.

ANNA. Yeah it is. "Now you are ready to rule your kingdom without me!"

BUN. Do it properly.

ANNA. Fine. "Now you have Excalibur, It is time for me to leave you. But know I will always be with you. Here."

And he gave Arthur an acorn. *(As* **ANNA***.)* An acorn? What a rubbish present.

BUN. Keep reading!

ANNA. "Now your kingdom is small, but over time it will grow, like the acorn grows into the oak. Whenever you feel alone, hold the acorn and remember me, and know I am with you. Difficult times are ahead. You must beware." *(As* **ANNA***.)* There's a picture of Morgana here!

BUN. Yeah.

ANNA. She's got like long twisty black hair and a purple dress. Honestly she looks mint.

BUN. She's evil, / remember.

ANNA. Yeah, yeah, evil.

BUN. Keep going.

ANNA. "The evil sorceress Morgana Le Fey will soon learn of Excalibur, and she will stop at nothing to take it from you. If Morgana gets her hands on Excalibur, Britain will fall. You must make sure it never claims it."

"And sure enough, in the wild outer reaches of Arthur's kingdom, Morgana was already lying in wait, gathering her dark powers, preparing to attack."

(As **ANNA** *reads,* **MRS PARSONS** *arrives to* **BUN***'s house.)*

Scene Four

BUN. I felt a bit better after that, having Anna to talk to. But I still didn't like to leave my room, no matter how much Dad tried to make me. And little did I know my own nemesis was on the horizon, coming to ruin my life forever. Not an evil sorceress, worse, it was…

… MRS PARSONS

MRS PARSONS. Lemon drizzle cake?

BUN. What?

MRS PARSONS. My mother always said it was rude to pay a visit without bringing a bottle of gin but it's a little early in the day for that so hey ho, lemon drizzle it is.

BUN. Who are you?

MRS PARSONS. Don't they teach you *manners* on this island? Pleased to meet you, too. I'm Mrs Parsons. I'm a teacher. Your Dad's asked me to come and have a little chat.

BUN. Why? What kind of teacher?

MRS PARSONS. You ask a lot of questions. Here, let's get you a piece of cake first. Now come on, chop chop, where are you?

BUN. Um.

MRS PARSONS. Speak up.

BUN. I'm here.

MRS PARSONS. Righto.

BUN. Are you blind, too?

MRS PARSONS. Yes.

BUN. Is that why you're here?

MRS PARSONS. I think this batch was particularly successful. People think its easy, lemon drizzle, but there's a knack to it. Hold your hand out. There.

BUN. Thanks… did you make it yourself?

MRS PARSONS. Of course. Mary Berry eat your heart out.

BUN. How?

MRS PARSONS. Oh, let me see, butter, sugar, lemon and eggs, fold in the flour, / oven at 180.

BUN. No, um, I mean…

MRS PARSONS. Do all that without looking? I have a magic wand.

*(**MRS PARSONS** takes out her audio labeller.)*

Well, its science really not magic. It's called an audio labeller. I put little electric labels on things and it reads them out.

(She demonstrates, holding it to her jumper.)

AUDIO LABELLER. Green jumper.

MRS PARSONS. But it feels a bit magic. Want a go? Here.

*(She gives **BUN** the audio describer.)*

I'm holding my arm out in front of you, there.

AUDIO LABELLER. Brown jacket.

BUN. Can you make it say anything?

MRS PARSONS. I suppose so. Within reason.

BUN. Cool.

MRS PARSONS. I'll be having that back, thank you.

BUN. So you're here cos of my accident?

MRS PARSONS. Your Dad thought I might be some help.

BUN. What, you teach people how to be blind?

MRS PARSONS. Something like that. Now, for starters, how about we get you out of that room of yours. I hear there's a party for the solstice coming up, down by the jetty.

BUN. No thanks.

MRS PARSONS. I've brought you a stick, we can talk through how to use it, maybe go for a walk, talk about the future

BUN. A stick? Like. One of those white ones?

MRS PARSONS. That's right. I call mine Sticky Minaj.

BUN. Absolutely not.

MRS PARSONS. You don't want one?

BUN. No!

MRS PARSONS. Why not?

BUN. It's embarrassing.

MRS PARSONS. Why?

BUN. No one else uses one.

MRS PARSONS. I use one.

BUN. Nobody else on the island, nobody else at my school

MRS PARSONS. There aren't any other visually impaired kids at your school?

BUN. You're the first blind person I've met.

MRS PARSONS. You were the first blind person you met. It was the same for me, when I lost my sight. Nobody I knew was blind. I'd never even seen any films or TV or anything with a blind person, read any books. I felt very alone. My situation was a little different. I had a degenerative condition in my retinas so I lost my sight over time. I think that's a bit different from you, isn't it? But I felt lonely, too.

BUN. I don't feel lonely.

MRS PARSONS. Oh, well that's good to hear. But your Dad says you're not getting out of the house? *(Beat.)* Not the most accessible place is it, Bryher?

BUN. It's the best place in the world.

MRS PARSONS. Oh, I'm sure it's lovely, just not really built for people like us.

BUN. Like us?

MRS PARSONS. Disabled people. It was the same / for me

BUN. Stop saying that.

MRS PARSONS. What?

BUN. 'It was the same'. It wasn't. You just said you lost your sight gradually over time. I fell and hit my head and nearly died and woke up like this. So stop saying you know what it's like because you don't.

(Beat.)

MRS PARSONS. Maybe you're right. But I do know that just because the way you *lost* your sight was traumatic, doesn't mean that *living* with your sight loss has to be.

BUN. Why are you even here? You've given me the stick, you've done that now, you can go.

MRS PARSONS. I run an SEN school, do you know what that is?

BUN. No.

MRS PARSONS. It means Special Educational Needs. It's a lovely place, on the mainland, just outside Exeter.

BUN. I don't have special educational needs.

MRS PARSONS. The students and lots of the teachers are visually impaired, like you.

BUN. I'm not leaving Bryher.

MRS PARSONS. You dad and I talked, and we / both think.

BUN. Dad wants this?

MRS PARSONS. It's not forever, just term times. You can meet new people, new friends.

BUN. I don't need new people I have people here.

MRS PARSONS. Bun. I know big change has already happened to you, and another one feels scary.

BUN. It's not scary, I have friends here, my life's here. The island's my *home.*

MRS PARSONS. That's why you're hiding in your room, is it?

BUN. I'm. I'm not.

MRS PARSONS. Can you get around the island, on your own? Safely? Like you used to? The best way you can learn to do all those things for yourself again is to come and learn with me, with us. You'll get your island back but you'll get more than that, too. There's a whole world out there, Bun. A whole world of people like you and me. And we can be a huge source of strength, joy, support to each other. You don't have to keep your world small to feel safe in it. There's a couple of months yet till term starts. Think about it.

Scene Five

BUN. And she left. Think about it? Leaving home, going to some stupid school and eating dry lemon drizzle and walking with a stick and being different my whole life? Dad, sending me away? The anger rose up in me again, like stinging nettles. It wasn't fair. I hadn't asked for any of this. Luckily now I had Anna to talk to. She came round mine and we sat on my bed again.

ANNA. You can't leave!

BUN. That's what I said!

ANNA. Bryher's the best place in the world.

BUN. That's what I said!

ANNA. And *Exeter?* That's *miles* away!

BUN. Three hundred amd thirty miles. And a boat and a train and a taxi.

ANNA. What are you going to do?

BUN. I don't know.

ANNA. Can't you talk to your Dad?

BUN. And say what? He's the one who wants me to go. Now I'm not his lucky charm anymore, he doesn't know what to do with me.

ANNA. Well... I've got something that might cheer you up.

BUN. Nothing could cheer me up.

ANNA. I'm going to put something on your ears, is that OK?

BUN. Yes?

ANNA. Here you go, headphones going on

(**ANNA** *puts headphones on* **BUN.**)

AUDIOBOOK. Whosoever pulls this sword from the stone is the rightful King of Britain!

BUN. *(Shouting over headphones.)* OH MY GOD!

ANNA. Ssh!

BUN. Oh my god! This is –!

ANNA. Yup.

BUN. You found it!

ANNA. Yup.

(Feeling the tape player.)

BUN. What *is* that?

ANNA. It's cassette player.

BUN. A *what?*

ANNA. I know. It's like ancient. I looked for the book everywhere online to download but couldn't find it, and then my mum said she used to listen to books on *tape* when she was a kid, so I went to the library and asked them but they hadn't even *heard* of it and I was honestly about to give up but then I saw this old second-hand bookshop by the harbour.

BUN. That's where I bought the book from!

ANNA. And they had one! And that's not even the weird bit, right. There was this old hippy dude with a big white beard at the counter and he was all.

OLD HIPPY DUDE. Didn't know you kids still listened to tapes.

ANNA. So I said, It's for my friend, Bun. It's his favourite. And then *he* said.

OLD HIPPY DUDE. Oh, I know Ben Bundle. How's his head?

BUN. Weird.

ANNA. And then he gave me this. It's an acorn. Here, hold out your hand.

BUN. An acorn?

ANNA. Yeah. I think he might have lost of his marbles

BUN. Anna! That's from the book!

ANNA. What?

BUN. Yeah! Which button is fast forward?

ANNA. This one.

BUN. Remember? After Arthur has the sword, he's ready to be king and Merlin leaves him, but when he goes he gives him an acorn.

ANNA. Oh yeah! *(Doing her silly* **MERLIN** *voice.)* 'Now your kingdom is small like a teeny beany acorn.'

BUN. Ssshh

AUDIOBOOK. "Now your kingdom is small, but over time it will grow, like the acorn grows into the oak."

ANNA. Woah, Bun, that can't be a coincidence.

BUN. What do you mean?

ANNA. I mean this guy was *old* and *beardy* and *super* wizardy.

BUN. Oh come on, you don't think that old hippy was Merlin, do you?

ANNA. He knew you! He knew all about your accident!

BUN. Everyone knows about my accident, I can't go anywhere everyone doesn't know about my accident.

ANNA. You know as well as I do that Bryher is a bit magic.

BUN. That is true. *(Beat.)* I'm not going to that school, Anna. I'm staying here.

ANNA. How?

BUN. I'm going to show them I don't need their special school or special help. I'm going to get around the island by myself. Then I can have my old life, exactly as it was, here on Bryher. If I can prove to them I can do it without them, they have to let me stay on the island, right?

ANNA. *(In her silly* **MERLIN** *voice.)* Sir Ben Bundle of Bryher, that is an excellent idea.

Scene Six

BUN. So, Anna and I got to work exploring the island. Turns out home wasn't so hard. I had like a memory-map in my head of where things were, and I could figure out tricks to make it easier, like I put stickers on the banister so I knew when I was at the top or bottom of the stairs. If I concentrated and went slowly at first, and so long as my Dad didn't keep leaving his slippers in the middle of the kitchen, before long I could find my way around the house pretty well.

Outside though... that was a different matter. The tiny island had never seemed so big before.

(**BUN** *takes a step outside and is hit with a wall of sound, people, wind, birds, ocean, boats.)*

I'd never noticed before how rough the paths were, how easy it was to trip, how uneven the steps were in town. Anna helped me.

ANNA. OK, we're at Gweal Hill. The sea is to the right, the path to the harbour is behind you.

BUN. And as we walked, I realised there were a lot of things I'd never even noticed about the island before. How the wind is strongest on your face up the top of Samson Hill. How quiet and peaceful Rushy Bay is. That the wind chimes in the tuck shop sing when it starts raining. How satisfying the *crunch* of the gravel on the farm track is under your feet. How Fraggle's café smells like vanilla. How you can *taste* the spray off the waves at Hell Bay. It's weird, I've been round this island thousands of times, but there were so many amazing things I'd never noticed.

And I'd never spent this much time with Anna before, just us. It was nice. Turns out she's alright, and kind of a nerd, like me.

ANNA. So the solstice is the shortest night of the year, when the sun's in the sky for the longest. And it only happens once a year. And then a rose moon is what happens when you get a full moon near the solstice, and this year we're getting a mega rose moon cause its gonna be a full moon on the *same night* as the solstice, and that hasn't happened in *hundreds of years* and I have a theory its gonna make the tides go crazy so I've been all mapping the tides in my star chart and comparing them with other years and if my calculations are correct, the tide will be so low it'll reveal some *secret islands,* hidden for centuries.

BUN. See what I mean? Nerd! It was great.

And the more we walked, the more I concentrated, the clearer my memory map became. Sometimes it even felt a bit like before.

ANNA. Chips at Fraggles?

BUN. Only if you're paying.

ANNA. Oh no Mr Jenkins is out, wearing his Speedo.

BUN. Gross!

ANNA. Hey, here comes a tourist!

TOURIST. Hello, I'm here for the solstice celebration tonight, where's the best place to watch from?

ANNA. Oh, I think at the very very very top of Gweal Hill, don't you Bun?

BUN. Oh absolutely. Just start going up the steep track and keep on walking.

TOURIST. Really?

ANNA. A hundred percent.

TOURIST. Well.... thank you.

ANNA. Enjoy!

(They laugh.)

BUN. And we'd listen to my tapes together. Sometimes we pretended to be Arthur.

AUDIOBOOK. Morgana sent a terrible beast to Camelot, a giant with the head of a dragon, fierce eyes that burnt into the soul and a foul pestilent breath. Arthur tightened his grip on Excalibur and let out a battle cry. 'AAAAAHHH!'

BUN & ANNA. AAAAAAHH!

AUDIOBOOK. With all his force he thrust his blade deep into the scales of the dragon-man's throat.

ANNA. Take *that* lizard lips!

AUDIOBOOK. And the giant fell.

BUN. See I *told* you it was the best book ever.

ANNA. It's growing on me. Time for an ice cream? Or have you got to get back?

BUN. Lemme see...

TALKING WATCH. The time is four twenty seven p.m.

ANNA. What is that?

BUN. Oh what, this old thing?

ANNA. Your watch talks to you?

BUN. Yeah. Cool right?

ANNA. How does it work?

BUN. I just press this button here.

TALKING WATCH. The time is four twenty eight p.m.

ANNA. Where'd you get it?

BUN. Well, um...

ANNA. What?

BUN. Mrs Parson's sent it.

ANNA. Mrs Parsons?? Our nemesis?

BUN. I know but it's actually really helpful. She sent me this box of stuff. I think she's trying to bribe me.

ANNA. You got cool blind swag and you didn't tell me? What else?

BUN. Uhh, oh yeah, this one's cool. A compass.

TALKING COMPASS. North east.

BUN. And if I spin around, like this.

TALKING COMPASS. East southeast south southwest west northwest.

*(**BUN** spins faster and the compass talks faster and faster and they laugh.)*

BUN. Remix!

*(**BUN** turns in different directions, making the compass keep up, maybe they 'sing' along with the compass remix.)*

ANNA. Big fish, little fish, cardboard box...

TALKING WATCH. The time is four thirty p.m.

ANNA. That's class.

BUN. Yeah. She also sent a voicenote.

ANNA. Yeah?

BUN. Yeah.

MRS PARSONS VOICENOTE. Hi Bun, hope you like the gadgets. I feel a bit like Q from James Bond. Looking forward to welcoming you here when term starts. Lots more to show you! Speak soon.

ANNA. When term starts? As if.

BUN. Yeah.

ANNA. Well joke's on her. We can use this stuff to help you stay put on Bryher, right?

BUN. Exactly! Vanquish her like the dragon man!

ANNA. Yeah! Like Morgana! She is *toast.* Hey, how does Arthur beat Morgana, maybe we can steal his ideas?

BUN. Well, Arthur doesn't actually beat Morgana.

ANNA. Of course he does.

BUN. Not really.

ANNA. What, the baddie wins?

BUN. Well. Sort of? Hang on, let me get the cassette.

ANNA. He has to defeat her. He has to keep Excalibur and protect the kingdom and keep stabbing dragon men in the face it's his *destiny.* Bun.

BUN. Hang on!

OK, so, this is the final battle, Arthur and Morgana's armies have met on the battlefield and the two of them are locked in combat.

(**BUN** *and* **ANNA** *sword fight.)*

AUDIOBOOK ARTHUR. We fought long and hard. Blood poured down my head, my neck, my arms ached, but I fought on, swinging Excalibur with the last of my strength.

It was no use.

ANNA. Seriously? Turn it up.

AUDIOBOOK ARTHUR. I staggered and fell to my knees on the dirt. I barely had strength to grip my sword by the hilt. I was finished.

ANNA. No!

BUN. Ssh!

AUDIOBOOK ARTHUR. I knew I had one last task; To keep Morgana from claiming Excalibur. I summoned the last of my dying strength and called my most loyal knight, Sir Bedevere, to my side, to ask one last act of service

ANNA. He *dies??* Arthur *dies* at the end??

BUN. Listen!

AUDIOBOOK ARTHUR. Bedevere! Sir Bedevere!

AUDIOBOOK BEDEVERE. Here, your majesty.

ANNA. Why would you read a book where the hero loses?

BUN. Sssh!

AUDIOBOOK ARTHUR. My friend, I am spent. The battle is lost. You must take Excalibur, now. Ride away from here as fast as you can, find the furthest, deepest, darkest lake and throw the sword into it, watch it sink.

ANNA. He can't!

AUDIOBOOK BEDEVERE. My lord, I cannot! Without Excalibur you're vulnerable, you'll die

BUN. He has to.

AUDIOBOOK ARTHUR. You must! If Morgana gets hold of Excalibur, she'll be undefeatable. Please. Do this for me.

BEDEVERE. My lord, I will.

ANNA. So Morgana wins? Bedevere just chucks the sword in a pond and leaves Arthur to die? Who writes this stuff?!

BUN. He doesn't die. Remember Merlin's promise?

MERLIN. I will return when you need me the most.

BUN. Merlin saves him. He magics him away to a dark cave somewhere super secret, beyond the shore, beyond time itself. Safe from Morgana.

ANNA. So... he's still out there somewhere?

BUN. Exactly.

ANNA. Just... hanging out?

BUN. Waiting.

ANNA. What for?

BUN. For when he's needed again. And Excalibur goes back into the lake.

ANNA. Can't Morgana just fish it out?

BUN. No. Lady Vivian, The Lady of Lake, has power in the water. Morgana knows her own magic won't work under the surface. She can't risk it. Excalibur is safe there.

ANNA. What a weird ending.

BUN. I like it. Cause its sort of like it doesn't end. Its like, really its only just begun.

ANNA. Doesn't help us out with Mrs Parsons though, does it?

BUN. We don't need help, we're doing it. We've been all round the island now, my memory maps pretty near finished.

ANNA. Kind of.

BUN. What?

ANNA. Well... there's one place we haven't been yet. The jetty.

BUN. Why would we go to the jetty?

ANNA. For the memory map.

BUN. But I don't need to know the jetty, I'm not getting on a boat, am I? I'm not leaving.

ANNA. But if we want to have a total memory map of the / island…

BUN. We've got the whole rest of the island, come on, lets go to Rushy Bay again.

ANNA. We've been there a hundred times already.

BUN. OK, we'll go up Gweal Hill again.

ANNA. I'll be with you, Bun, it's safe.

BUN. I know.

ANNA. I mean. Nothing bad's gonna / happen.

BUN. Yeah I know, would you drop / it?

ANNA. I mean the solstice party's at the jetty, you don't wanna miss that.

BUN. I don't wanna go.

ANNA. But we always go, and this year…

BUN. Yeah, yeah, yeah mega rose moon whatever boring.

ANNA. There's nothing to be scared of, Bun.

BUN. I said leave it!

ANNA. Bun.

BUN. What, you want me to fall and hit my head so you can snog me again?

ANNA. I didn't / snog you.

BUN. "Oh no, Bun's in trouble!"

ANNA. That's not / funny.

BUN. "He's all cold and floppy".

ANNA. Stop it.

BUN. "Luke call an ambulance I'm doing mouth to / mouth" *(He makes kissing sounds.)*

ANNA. It was horrible, it was the worst moment of my life, I thought I'd killed you.

BUN. What?

ANNA. Nothing.

BUN. You thought you'd killed me?

ANNA. It doesn't matter Bun, let's go, chips, I'm buying...

BUN. It was me jumped off the pier without looking.

ANNA. Yeah I know

BUN. Then what?

ANNA. Or an ice cream maybe

BUN. Anna!

ANNA. I made you do it.

BUN. What?

ANNA. You just wanted to read your book. If I hadn't made fun of you, you wouldn't have jumped and you wouldn't have hit your head and...

BUN. You think it's your fault?

ANNA. I ...yeah. I'm sorry.

BUN. Is that why you're doing all this? Cause you feel guilty?

ANNA. No! Bun, that's not / why.

BUN. The walks, the tapes, everything, it's just cause you feel guilty.

ANNA. It isn't, Bun. I mean. I do feel guilty but that's / not the only reason.

BUN. Just cause you feel sorry for me!

ANNA. No, Bun, where are you going?

BUN. Home.

ANNA. Bun, stop.

BUN. I don't need your pity.

ANNA. Don't be like that. Bun! At least let me take you home.

BUN. No. You've done enough. Pretending to be my friend just to make yourself feel better. Well I don't need you.

ANNA. Bun you'll get lost on your own! Bun.

(**BUN** *walks away.*)

BUN. But I kept walking away. I'd been relying on her too much, if I wanted to stay I had to prove I could do it on my own, by myself, that was the plan.

Come on. Bun, the memory map, use it, you can do it. The sea is louder to my right, the ground feels like its climbing upwards, this must be the way up towards Gweal Hill. Slowly, easy. There's a bit where it gets steeper where you have to keep left to avoid the bushes. There. And a big rock at the top. Ah –

I tripped.

Stinging nettles.

I could feel the wind. Suddenly it was *freezing* cold. I stuffed my hands in my pockets... the acorn! It wasn't there! I must have dropped it when I fell, where was it? I scrabbled in the grass. Please, please, please.

TOURIST. Hey, you! You're the boy who gave me bad directions!

BUN. Oh no! The tourist from before! Quick, find it, find it...

TOURIST. You lied to me, and I've wasted precious time...

BUN. Found it!

TOURIST. Stop right there! Hey! What is that?

BUN. Nothing gotta go, bye – hey, let go of my arm!

TOURIST. Is that... the acorn? It can't be!

BUN. Let go! I'm sorry about the directions OK if / you go to the jetty.

TOURIST. Where did you get this? Who gave this to you? Tell me!

BUN. Nobody, let me go...

TOURIST. Who gave it to you?

BUN. An old hippy dude with a big white beard, OK?

TOURIST. Merlin.

BUN. Merlin? He let me go.

TOURIST. No. No, no, no. You're the messenger? You can't be, that's impossible, you're a child.

BUN. The messenger, what? What are you talking about?

TOURIST. Merlin told me to come to this island. To seek out the solstice. That I'd know the messenger by the acorn he carried.

BUN. What messenger?

TOURIST. He didn't tell you? Why does he always have to be so *mysterious*, honestly, wizards! Not *everything* has to be a metaphor, *Merlin*.

BUN. Who are you?

BEDEVERE. My name is Sir Bedevere, Knight of the Round Table and loyal subject to Arthur, King of Britain.

BUN. OK, very funny.

BEDEVERE. What?

BUN. Bedevere, right, sure, and I'm Sir Lancelot.

BEDEVERE. Lancelot was a lot taller...

BUN. Did Anna make you do this?

BEDEVERE. I don't know anyone called Anna. Please, listen. We don't have much time. Tonight the solstice and the full moon coincide for the first time in hundreds of years resulting in a mega rose moon. The tide will be so low it will reveal a secret island, hidden for centuries.

BUN. Anna was *right?!*

BEDEVERE. I don't know anyone called Anna! Listen. Arthur, the high King of Britain, has been hiding all these years on that island. And I need your help to get something to him, before Morgana gets to him first.

BUN. Morgana?

BEDEVERE. She's found him. She's been waiting all this time for the island to appear so she can finish him, once and for all. And he's out there, defenceless... unless you can help me return his mighty sword, Excalibur, to his hands.

BUN. Sir Bedevere threw Excalibur into the deepest, darkest, furthest lake he could find. You're not fooling me

BEDEVERE. No. I didn't.

BUN. What?

BEDEVERE. I lied. I told Arthur I would do just as you say. That I would throw away the sword where nobody would find it. But I couldn't do it. I broke my promise and I kept the sword hidden all these years. And good thing too! Because tonight he'll need it. Please. You need to help me get the sword back to him!

BUN. This isn't funny. Just cause I can't see you, you can't laugh at me like this.

BEDEVERE. You don't believe me? Hold the sword yourself.

(**BEDEVERE** *hands* **BUN** *the sword.)*

BUN. I took the hilt of the sword in my hand and... Suddenly I felt this *power* running through me, all through my veins like lightning, fiery sparks exploding in my head right down to the tips of my fingers and toes like I was magic, like I could do anything. It fit my fingers as if it had been built for me.

Aah!

BEDEVERE. Do you believe me now?

BUN. This... This sword is... Excalibur?

BEDEVERE. The very same. And you must take the sword and return it to it's rightful bearer. To King Arthur himself.

BUN. Me?

BEDEVERE. Merlin told me he was sending a messenger. That I would know them by the sign of the acorn. You carry the acorn. It has to be you.

BUN. You must have the wrong person. I can't do that.

BEDEVERE. Merlin wouldn't have sent you unless you were equal to the task. He's an odd fish but even I have to admit, he's generally right.

BUN. Merlin chose me... how do I find Arthur?

BEDEVERE. When the sun sets, and the rose moon rises, a new island will emerge from the water. But you have to be quick; Morgana knows it's location and will be on her way there as well. And by sunrise the island will disappear again. Please. We have to help him.

BUN. I'll do what I can, I'll try

BEDEVERE. And... will you tell him I'm sorry?

BUN. I will. Bedevere?

How do I find the island? Bedevere?

But he was gone. I held the sword. I felt the magic of it prickle all over me. The air was getting cooler, soon the sun would set. I had to hurry. Merlin chose me. But to get to the island... I'd need to take a boat. From the jetty. I knew I couldn't do it alone. I needed Anna.

Scene Seven

BUN. I got to her house as quickly as I could.

Anna! Anna!

ANNA. Go away.

BUN. Anna!

ANNA. I'm not talking to you.

BUN. I need your help.

ANNA. Oh so *now* you need my help!

BUN. I'm not happy about it either!

ANNA. Go home.

BUN. I need to go to the jetty.

ANNA. Thought you said the solstice was stupid and boring / and.

BUN. Anna it's not YOU WERE RIGHT.

(Beat.)

ANNA. OK say more.

BUN. There is a secret island. Bryher *is* magic. That man *was* Merlin. They're all here, Bedevere, Morgana, Arthur himself! And look, Excalibur!

ANNA. Bun what... where did you get that?

BUN. I'll explain on the way, there's not much time. We can fight again in the morning but right now we have to go.

ANNA. OK. But I'm bringing my star journal.

BUN. Fine! Come on, or we'll miss the tide!

ANNA. The tide? We're going out to sea? Bun!

(To us.)

BUN. I explained everything best I could on the way.

ANNA. I knew my calculations were correct! Hey, if we help Arthur, maybe Merlin will help us. Help you stay here on Bryher.

BUN. Yeah, maybe...

ANNA. OK, Bun. We're here. The jetty. Everyone's over at the bandstand, the fishermen are singing. Your Dad's there. What now?

BUN. Where's his boat?

(They are singing; maybe **[HAERD TIMES FISHERMEN]**.*)*

ANNA. It's tied up at the end of the jetty.

BUN. OK. OK. Take me to it.

ANNA. You sure you're ready?

BUN. I ...I think so. I don't want to fall. If they just made the ground at the edges of the jetty feel different to the ground in the middle of the jetty, then I'd know where the edges were and I wouldn't need help!

ANNA. Well. For now, if you want we can pretend we're not not in a fight and you can hold my arm? And I'll keep you away from the edge.

BUN. OK. Thank you.

DAD. Bun, is that you?

ANNA. He's seen us! Your Dad! He's coming over! We have to move, now Bun

BUN. We stepped out onto the rickety wood. For the first time since I came home from the hospital, I felt the wood under my shoes. I heard the squeaky ropes of my Dad's boat as we drew closer.

ANNA. You're sure about this, Bun? I mean, can you still sail?

BUN. I have to. Merlin chose me, he gave me the acorn, so that I could bring Excalibur back to Arthur. I need to try.

ANNA. OK, quick, get in!

BUN. Untie the ropes.

ANNA. The engine won't start...

DAD. Bun?

BUN. It's Dad! We'll have to row, hand me the oars.

ANNA. OK, go, row!

BUN. We pushed off from the jetty and out into the open water. I could hear the water sloshing against the hull, feel the boat roll under me and for a moment it was like old times, with Dad, out at sea bringing in the pots, his lucky charm. I forgot how much I loved this.

ANNA. Where to?

BUN. Look for new islands revealed by the tides.

ANNA. Aye, aye, captain. Heave ho, hard to starboard...

(We hear a woman's laughter.)

What was that?

BUN. I don't know.

MORGANA. Off for a little midnight fishing trip? How exciting.

ANNA. Is that...?

BUN. It's Morgana! Where is she?

*(**MORGANA** laughs again.)*

ANNA. I don't know, it's like she's *everywhere.*

MORGANA. After all these years, this is all that stands between me and Excalibur!

BUN. We have to find the island.

ANNA. There! Bun at the end of the sandbar, that must be it.

BUN. How far?

ANNA. Not far, almost there. Row harder!

BUN. I am rowing harder!

ANNA. Row harderer then!

MORGANA. A little girl with a star journal and a boy who can't see me coming.

ANNA. Wait, no, no no.

BUN. What?

ANNA. The fog's rolling in! I've never seen fog like it. Bun. I can't see anything. I cant even see Bryher behind us. I don't know where we are. I don't know where we're going! Why did your favourite book have to be so scary!

BUN. Wait, let's use the talking compass!

COMPASS. South East, East.

BUN. Turn!

COMPASS. North East, North, north West.

BUN. Straight ahead! Go!

COMPASS. North west.

ANNA. I think it's there, Bun, in the mist, keep going.

(A thud as **MORGANA** *lands in the boat.)*

MORGANA. That's right, Bun, you're so close. Closer than you think.

ANNA. Bun... she's... she's here. She's here! She's in the boat. She's just like in the pictures, Bun. Get back!

MORGANA. Good evening children. Enjoying the solstice, are we? Merlin's outdone himself this time. I know he likes an underdog but this is ridiculous.

BUN. I won't give you the sword!

MORGANA. Oh you will. You don't have a choice. Now, you can do it willingly, or you can do it painfully. Which would you prefer?

BUN. Neither.

MORGANA. It's not fair, is it, Bun? You didn't ask for any of this.

BUN. What?

MORGANA. This is what he does, Merlin. He picks and chooses, no regard for what people want. There you are living your happy quiet life, when along comes Merlin, hands you an acorn and sweeps you up in something terrible. No wonder you're sad. No wonder you're angry. No wonder you're scared.

BUN. I'm not.

MORGANA. Oh but we both know you are.

(**MORGANA** *magically plays a recording of* **BUN** *from earlier, saying 'I hate it. I just want to go back to how I was' 'Obviously it's not fine, obviously it's not going to be fine!' 'I don't feel very lucky' 'I want to be normal'.)*

BUN. No. No, that's... that's not...

ANNA. Bun, don't listen to her, please

MORGANA. Little girl, I think you've already done *more* than enough, don't you?

BUN. Stop that!

MORGANA. You don't want this, Bun. You want to be back in your bed, in your room, on your island, safe and sound. I can do that for you, Bun. Give me the sword and all of this goes away...

BUN. No! I don't feel that way anymore! This is where I'm supposed to be, and I won't let you take the sword!

MORGANA. Well then I suppose I'll have to kill you.

ANNA. SAY HELLO TO MY LITTLE STAR JOURNAL!

(Smack.)

MORGANA. Ow!

BUN. Anna?

ANNA. I hit her with the star journal, I think it just made her angry.

MORGANA. YOU WHELPS!

ANNA. Ah!

BUN. Suddenly the boat was rocked by a huge freak wave, sending us all flying. The water slammed against the side of the boat, I tasted the spray on my lips. I remembered. The Lady of the Lake has power in the water. Morgana's magic would be weaker there.

MORGANA. I HAVE WAITED HUNDREDS OF YEARS I WILL NOT WAIT ANY LONGER!

BUN. Then come and take it!

ANNA. Bun, wait!

BUN. I felt for the side of the boat and heaved myself up onto the edge. The waves were furious. I held Excalibur firmly in my hands. For a moment I stopped, I was afraid. Afraid of falling. Then I felt Morgana snatch at my ankles, I took a deep breath and I jumped, I flew,

SPLASH.

Down.

Into the water.

ANNA. Bun! No!

BUN. I clung to the sword with all my might. I heard Morgana *SPLASH* crash into the water behind me, she clutched at my ankles, I kicked and tried to swim to the surface. The sword was so heavy, it pulled me under. But I couldn't let go. The water rushed in my nose and my mouth, stung my eyes. I felt Morgana's hands unclasp, she floated away from me… I couldn't breathe… everything felt fuzzy… I held on to the sword and felt myself sinking…

ANNA. Bun!

AUDIOBOOK MERLIN. I will return when you need me the most.

*(**BUN** takes a huge breath and coughs and splutters.)*

ANNA. You're OK!

BUN. What happened, where am I?

ANNA. The boat capsized. I swam after you and pulled you ashore. We're on the island, Bun! We're in a cave.

BUN. What about the sword?

ANNA. It's here, Bun, you saved it. And. You're not gonna believe who's here. It's King Arthur!

ARTHUR. Well, well, well, Ben Bundle of Bryher. You certainly know how to make an entrance.

BUN. King Arthur! Really?

ANNA. A hundred percent. Actually.

BUN. Your majesty… *(He kneels.)* It's… It's an *honour*

ARTHUR. Oh I think we're beyond *ceremony,* come on, I'm going to hug you. If that's OK?

BUN. OK…!

ANNA. Bun's your number one fan.

BUN. Shut up.

ANNA. What! It's true. He's got all your books.

ARTHUR. I don't have any of his I'm afraid.

BUN. Well, um, I've never actually written one.

ARTHUR. Oh, you must, I think everyone has a book in / them...

ANNA. Um guys... Morgana!

BUN. Morgana! Where is she?

ARTHUR. Quite right, The Lady of thc Lake can hold her, but not for long, we must act quickly.

BUN. Here! Excalibur! You have to take it. Now! Defeat her, before its too late!

ARTHUR. Merlin didn't tell you?

BUN. Tell me what?

ARTHUR. Why does he always have to be so *mysterious*. Honestly, wizards. You're not here to return Excalibur to *me*.

BUN. But...

ARTHUR. Do you know the story of how I became King? How the sword was stuck fast in the stone and only I had the power to pull it free?

BUN. Yes, but...

ARTHUR. So it will be again. You must thrust Excalibur into the rock behind you, to keep it safe from Morgana, forever.

BUN. But... Merlin sent me to give it back to you.

ARTHUR. Bun. I'm an old man, now. I've been hiding away on this island for hundreds of years. I'm changed.

ANNA. He's right, Bun, he looks super old and sort of haggard?

ARTHUR. Thank you, Anna. I can't defeat Morgana with might anymore. Even if I could take Excalibur, she'd only take it from me. It's more important we make sure she cannot claim it. Which is why you must take it and stick it, fast, in the stone.

BUN. No!

ANNA. Bun...

BUN. You need it! The sword is your power, what will you do without it?

ARTHUR. Well. I'll have to find a new way to be strong. The world has changed, Bun. It's no longer a place for swords and sorcery. Morgana cannot accept that. I can.

BUN. You do it, then. Here.

ARTHUR. I can't. It must be you.

BUN. Why?

ARTHUR. Merlin chose you.

BUN. But *why?* Why me? Why does it have to be me?

(Beat.)

ARTHUR. I wondered that myself. When I pulled the sword out of the stone and became king. "Why me? I didn't ask for this." I still don't know. I'll never know. Sometimes there is no 'why'. My whole life changed in an instant, and I had to change with it. There was so much I missed, but so much I gained. New friends, new adventures. So many ways I grew. And I sense that in you. You are equal to this task.

BUN. How do you know that?

ARTHUR. Look at what you've already accomplished! More than many of my knights ever did. I swear, some were really only in it for the feasting.

BUN. What if I can't do it?

ANNA. We're here with you. We'll help.

ARTHUR. We are at your service.

ANNA. You can do it, Bun.

BUN. OK. I'll try. *(To us.)* I held the sword, tight. Arthur led me to the wall of the cave. I put out a hand to feel the cold wet stone in front of me.

ARTHUR. Goodbye, old friend. Time to sleep once more.

(The sounds from the **AUDIOBOOK** *return.)*

AUDIOBOOK. *The boy approached. He reached out his hand. The hilt fit his fingers as if it had been built for him. A hush fell. The sword slipped through the rock easily, as if the stone were butter.*

BUN. I did it.

ANNA. You did it!

ARTHUR. The sword will sleep here, and the Kingdom will be safe. Thank you, Ben Bundle of Bryher.

*(***ANNA** *coughs.)*

And Lady Anna of Bryher. What a mess this all was! If only Bedevere had done what I asked him in the first place…

BUN. He did what he thought was right at the time. And when he realised he was wrong, he fixed it the best way he knew how. He's spent enough time feeling guilty. You should forgive him. So… so he can forgive himself. Don't you think so, Anna?

ANNA. Yeah. That would be good.

ARTHUR. You really like giving orders to a king, don't you? Risky. But you're right. Bedevere's an old, dear friend, and I forgive him.

ANNA. What about Morgana?

ARTHUR. Merlin has arranged a new home for me, far from here. Morgana will search for hundreds more years before she finds me again. Now, let's get you home.

BUN. But my Dad's boat, we wrecked it! Nevermind Morgana, my Dad's gonna kill us.

ARTHUR. We'll see about that.

ANNA. Bun! The boat! It's back, good as new!

ARTHUR. Wizards. They get stuff done.

BUN. Give me a hand up, Anna?

ANNA. Course. I'll steer, you row?

BUN. Perfect.

ANNA. You coming, Arthur? We need to be quick, before the sun rises and the island disappears!

ARTHUR. Yes... I suppose I should...

BUN. What's wrong?

ARTHUR. I haven't left this island in hundreds of years. It's been my home. I'm a little scared to leave it.

BUN. Yeah. But. You can't stay in one place forever. And there's no dragon-men anymore so you don't have to worry about them. Your kingdom's changed a lot since you went into hiding. There's a whole new world out there.

ARTHUR. A new adventure... help an old man up into the boat, would you?

BUN. I reached for the oars but before I could touch them the boat began moving, all on its own. The Lady of the Lake, helping us one last time.

We flew back over the water, safely back to Bryher, to home. And we tied Dad's boat back up at the jetty, like it had never left.

Here we are, this is Bryher.

ARTHUR. A beautiful place.

BUN. Yeah. It's magic.

ARTHUR. Well. This is where we say goodbye.

ANNA. Bun! The old hippy guy from the bookshop is waiting up by Fraggles! And that tourist we helped out this morning.

BUN. Merlin and Bedevere.

ARTHUR. Thank you for all you've done for me. It was an honour to meet you both.

BUN. The acorn! You could give it back to Merlin.

ARTHUR. Keep it. And remember me.

BUN. Your majesty –

ANNA. He's gone.

BUN. The sun's come up. The island must be hidden again.

ANNA. How'd you tell?

BUN. I can sort of feel the light on me. And I can hear the birds waking up.

(We listen to the birds.)

It wasn't your fault, Anna.

(Beat.)

ANNA. OK.

BUN. It wasn't. Like Arthur said. It was just an accident. And if it hadn't happened, we'd never have become such good friends. And. I'm glad we are.

ANNA. Yeah. Me too. And hey – there's no way Mrs Parsons can send you away from the island now! If you can do *all of that* without her you definitely don't need that special school, right? You can stay on Bryher!

BUN. I want to go.

ANNA. What?

BUN. Anna, I want to go.

ANNA. No!

BUN. To meet new people, other blind people, learn how to do new things, explore a new place. I don't want to just read about people doing brave things. I want to do them. A new adventure.

And I'll be back for holidays. And we can go for our walks all over the island.

ANNA. But, Bun...

BUN. I know, I know, you'll miss me. You'll be heartbroken. Your world will be empty.

ANNA. Alright, get over yourself.

BUN. I'll miss you. But just think of all the gadgets I'll bring back from Mrs Parsons.

ANNA. Like a deadly stun gun or a hoverboard or a pocket toaster.

BUN. Maybe.

ANNA. Well. I can try and make the island better. Safer, easier for you. For when you come back. If you'd like. Bun... you're sure?

BUN. Yes. This is my choice.

So I told Dad I was ready to go. And we called Mrs Parsons. My nemesis. Not my nemesis anymore. She's actually really nice. When summer ended, I packed a bag. I left the house, down the path through the field to where the road is proper, past Luke's house and the tuck shop and the shouting fishermen, along the rickety old jetty. Dad and Anna and Luke and everyone on the island came to say goodbye. I led the way, with my white stick. It helps me get around. I've decided to name it. Not Sticky Minaj. Mine's called Excalibur. I waved to the crowd. I felt like a hero. Dad carried my suitcase for me and held my hand as we walked along the jetty.

Hey, Dad, the floor is different! The texture's different at the edges, so I won't fall in!

DAD. Yeah, uh... Anna told me your idea so me and some of the other fishermen put it in this morning. I hope it's OK?

BUN. It's... thank you.

DAD. And... I've looked it up online and there's lots of ideas on how to adjust my boat for. For blind sailors. So when you're back you can come out with me again. Only if you want to, mind.

BUN. I'd love to.

DAD. I, uh, I'm going to hug you now.

BUN. OK.

DAD. Anna said I should tell you when I'm going to hug you.

BUN. Thanks.

DAD. So this is me telling you / I'm going to hug you.

BUN. Just, OK you can hug me!

DAD. Here. I'm proud of you, Bun. You'll always be my lucky charm.

ANNA. Bun!

BUN. Anna, hey. I have something for you.

ANNA. The acorn!

BUN. Will you plant it for me, so it can grow?

ANNA. I will. Go on, don't miss your boat, shrimpy.

BUN. Classic Gemini.

ANNA. See you in the holidays. Next round of chips is on you.

BUN. I climbed up onto the ferry

MRS PARSONS. Well, Bun. Are you ready?

BUN. Yes. Thank you Mrs Parsons.

MRS PARSONS. You can call me Viv, if you like. Outside of term time anyway.

BUN. Viv?

MRS PARSONS. That's my name, Viv. Short for Vivian. But nobody calls me Vivian except my wife when I'm in trouble

BUN. Your name is Vivian? Like the Lady of the Lake!

MRS PARSONS. Who?

BUN. That Lady of the Lake!

MRS PARSONS. She a friend of yours?

BUN. No, she's from The Legend of King Arthur. She's the queen of the elves who gives him the magic sword, Excalibur.

MRS PARSONS. Really? She sounds impressive. I don't know that story.

BUN. It's really good.

MRS PARSONS. Well. We've got a long journey. Maybe you could tell it to me?

(A song;)

PULL FOR THE SHORE, SAILOR, PULL FOR THE SHORE!
HEED NOT THE ROLLING WAVES, BUT BEND TO THE OAR;
SAFE IN THE LIFE BOAT, SAILOR, CLING TO SELF NO MORE!
LEAVE THE POOR OLD STRANDED WRECK,
AND PULL FOR THE SHORE!

BUN. And so I sailed off towards the horizon, towards a new life. I had no idea the adventures that were awaiting me. If I'd fight a dragon man or make a coat out of faces. Maybe I'll get this audiobook published, and sold in shops. Maybe it will make someone else feel brave, like King Arthur made me. Maybe I'll just learn to make a really brilliant drizzle cake. The best part about my story is that it's only just begun.

Lightning Source UK Ltd.
Milton Keynes UK
UKHW020939221022
410917UK00013B/436